You Can't Take It With You So Get Organized

A Guide For Organizing Your Important Information

CAROLE A. WAKEFIELD

authorHOUSE®

AuthorHouse™
1663 Liberty Drive, Suite 200
Bloomington, IN 47403
www.authorhouse.com
Phone: 1-800-839-8640

First published by AuthorHouse 5/15/2008
ISBN: 978-1-4343-7458-5 (e)
ISBN: 978-1-4343-7164-5 (sc)

Printed in the United States of America
Bloomington, Indiana

This book is printed on acid-free paper.

ORGANIZATION! ORGANIZATION! ORGANIZATION! We all keep our personal information in various places. The question is: Can anyone other than yourself locate your documents, insurance policies, investments and banking information? The bigger question is: Can you locate them?

This book provides the means by which YOU can ORGANIZE your important information. The work sheets guide you toward the data required to track your financial, personal and family information. Consequently, by completing this book, your personal representative or executor will immediately know who to contact, how to access your information, and how to maintain or distribute your finances and personal property.

STATEMENT OF LIMITED LIABILITY
PLEASE READ CAREFULLY

You Can't Take It With You So Get Organized
(A Guide For Organizing Your Important Information)

ACCOUNTING & FINANCIAL INFORMATION, LEGAL, MEDICAL AND PROBATE DOCUMENTS MAY VARY FROM STATE TO STATE. CONSULT WITH YOUR PROFESSIONALS.

- _____ Have you advised anyone what to do in the event you and your spouse are incapacitated or die simultaneously?

- _____ Do you have a current Will? Without a Will, a person is considered to have died "intestate," and his or her property will be distributed in accordance with the special provisions of the state in which the deceased resided; distribution may not necessarily be the preferences of the deceased.

- _____ Are your beneficiary designations current (life insurance, 401K, IRAs, estate plans, Wills, deferred compensation plans, defined benefits plans (pensions), annuity contracts)? Review these with your accounting, legal, financial, tax and insurance advisors.

- _____ Do you have a Directive to Physicians & Family or Surrogates or a Living Will?

- _____ Do you have a Medical Power of Attorney?

- _____ Do you have your medical history available?

- _____ Do you have a list of your current medications?

- _____ Do you have a Power of Attorney?

- _____ Do you have a current list of your passwords for any accounts or services?

- _____ Do you have a list of recurring bills to be paid?

- _____ Do you have a signatory(ies) on checking/savings account(s) and safe deposit box(es) other than your spouse? Are the accounts designated "Payable on Death" or "Joint Tenants with Rights of Survivorship?"

- _____ Do you have a list of your various insurance policies (health, disability, life, homeowners, auto, and the like), stocks, bonds, properties, etc., and how to contact your agents?

- _____ Do you know the location of birth certificates, military records, Wills, insurance policies, checkbooks, safe deposit box keys, etc.?

- _____ Do you have a list of your personal property (e.g., jewelry, furniture, antiques, artwork, china, silver, etc.) and your preferred disposition upon your death?

- _____ Do you have a list of family members and friends who need to be notified upon your death?

- _____ Do you have contact information for your minister and a funeral home?

- _____ Do you have an obituary written or information available for someone to write the obituary?

- _____ Do you have your funeral and memorial service planned?

- _____ Do you have a list of current credit/debit card numbers and customer service numbers (in the event of credit/debit card loss or theft)?

- _____ Do you have information available regarding your ancestors (e.g., names, birth dates, and places of birth)?

YOU CAN'T TAKE IT WITH YOU SO GET ORGANIZED
(A GUIDE FOR ORGANIZING YOUR IMPORTANT INFORMATION)

INSTRUCTIONS

- This book is designed for record keeping. Recording information in pencil will allow for changes and corrections.

- Compile appropriate information. Start at the beginning of this book and proceed through the sections one at a time.

- After recordation, make a hard copy and deposit in a secure place (other than your home) in the event of fire, flood or other destruction of your home. If the original is destroyed, reproduction will be easier—out of date though it may be. Retrieve this copy from your secure place and update it every few months. This secure place may be a safe deposit box, your office, a safe, a relative, or a satellite computer.

- This book is also available on a CD and can be downloaded to a computer for easy, periodic updates. To order a CD, go to www.organizeforever.com.

- Due to sensitivity of the information contained herein, keep this book in a safe place.

YOU CAN'T TAKE IT WITH YOU SO GET ORGANIZED
(A GUIDE FOR ORGANIZING YOUR IMPORTANT INFORMATION)

Being a somewhat obsessive-compulsive person, I prepared this book for my daughter, Amy, and son, Craig. It began as the "Valuable Papers" (See Section 5, now known as "Important Information") 10 or 15 years ago so that I could organize our family accounts, investments, insurance, properties, etc. Our son and daughter would laugh and groan each time my husband and I went out of town because I would call to remind them where the "Valuable Papers" were. Over the years, they have grown very weary of the "Valuable Papers" reminder.

They can laugh all they want, but at least I know that when they need this information, which will be upon my and/or my husband's incapacitation or death, they will have the information necessary to effectuate any contracts, sign any documents and file any legal papers without searching through files, papers, safe deposit boxes, etc. When their dad and I depart this world, this book will make their lives much easier and less stressful.

If your children are your heirs, do them a favor by assigning (as fairly and carefully as you can) personal property to them. Family is everything. Relationships are more important than things. However, when money and "things" are involved, relationships are often forgotten. Relieve your children of this possibility. Prepare your children and grandchildren for the future armed with integrity and compassion. Pitting them against one another does not serve them well.

It is my hope that this book will be helpful to my generation as well as younger generations, thereby avoiding family disagreements. With this information at hand, you may experience peace of mind knowing what you have, where it is located and that you have done all you can to maintain family relationships.

A portion of the net proceeds from the sale of this book will be donated to selected charities.

ACKNOWLEDGEMENTS

It is with GREAT love, recognition and appreciation for my husband, Dave, who supported me in this endeavor (even though he laughed at my obsessive and compulsive organization; the rest of my family laughed as well). My son, Craig, and daughter, Amy, also made their contributions and offered their support (a few wisecracks, too).

I would also like to acknowledge and thank my good friends, Joyce and Tom Thompson, Sarah Olfers, and Pat Webb, for motivating me to write this book. My cousin, Pat Smith, was also very encouraging, and Marina Pita, Sharon Bass and Bradshaw-Carter Funeral Home were helpful in providing information. As well, I would like to thank Cody Crow, Virginia Fischer and Susan Alexander for their contributions.

Jean Allen, an Atlanta, Georgia attorney with whom I worked in the '60s and '70s, used to make the comment to wives whose husbands had died, "Before you cry, go to the bank!" In other words, find out what you need to sustain yourself financially before succumbing to grief.

Hopefully this book will assist the many unorganized people as well as those who are organized.

Contents

SECTION 1

What may be necessary in the event of the INCAPACITATION of

_____

OR the Simultaneous INCAPACITATION of

&
_____

- **IMMEDIATELY** provide Living Will, Directive to Physicians & Family or Surrogates, or Medical Power of Attorney **(See Section 6 – Location)** to doctor(s) and hospital(s) **(See Section 5 – Important Information).**

- Provide Medical History, Family Medical History **(See following pages)** and health insurance information to doctor(s) and hospital(s) **(See Section 5 – Important Information).**

- Locate Power of Attorney or any document empowering you to act in a legal capacity. **(Section 6 - Location)**.

- Review **Section 3 - Personal Bills**. Make deposits as necessary to checking account(s). Keep all bill payments current.

- Check **Section 4 - Passwords** for banking, credit/debit cards, online bill pay or any accounts or services.

- Check **Section 5 - Important Information** for doctors, attorneys, financial institutions, bank and stock accounts, health and disability insurance, properties, etc.

- Review any disability insurance policies. **(See Section 5 – Important Information).**

SECTION 1
MEDICAL HISTORY

for _____

Last Update _____

Medications	Medications	Vitamins & Herbs

Doctor/Clinic	Phone #	Address	Date(s)	Reason	Result

SECTION 1
MEDICAL HISTORY

for _____

Doctor/Clinic	Phone #	Address	Date(s)	Reason	Result

SECTION 1
MEDICAL HISTORY

for _____

Doctor/Clinic	Phone #	Address	Date(s)	Reason	Result

SECTION 1
FAMILY MEDICAL HISTORY
for _____

Last Update _____

Name	Relationship	Medical History	Cause Of Death

SECTION 1
FAMILY MEDICAL HISTORY
for _____

Name	Relationship	Medical History	Cause Of Death

NOTES:

SECTION 2

What may be necessary in the event of the DEATH of

_____

OR the Simultaneous DEATHS of

_____ & _____

- See Section 9 – Funeral & Memorial Services, Contact Numbers for Family & Friends & Obituary.

- In some areas of the U.S., if death occurs in a hospital within 24 hours after admission, the Medical Examiner is contacted; after 48 hours, the funeral home is called. If a person dies at home under hospice care, a nurse will call the funeral home. If someone dies unexpectedly at home, call 911; police will call the Medical Examiner. If the deceased was in an automobile accident, the Medical Examiner is called. The Death Certificate will be provided by the funeral home to the doctor. Check in your area for procedures.

- Determine the required number and order Death Certificates from the funeral home. Order a minimum of 10, more if there are multiple insurance policies, investment and bank accounts, etc. (See Section 5-Important Information). When reordering, the cost increases.

- Investigate the cost of funerals as prices may vary in different areas. Verify whether cremation occurs on funeral home premises or elsewhere.

- In a number of states, there are funeral homes that have a newspaper obituary account and receive a discount. On occasion the discount is passed along to the families. By allowing the funeral home to place your obituary, you may save money. Check with your funeral home.

- Provide attorney with Will(s) (See Section 6 - Location). An attorney will advise regarding probate requirements.

- See the following section, "General Information Regarding Probate."

- See Section 5 - Important Information for financial institutions, bank accounts, stock accounts, life insurance, properties, etc.

- Personal Bills (See Section 3 - Personal Bills). After death, any Power of Attorney will be invalid. An executor will need to assume this responsibility.

- Check Section 4 - Passwords for banking, credit/debit cards, online bill pay, services, etc.

- Contact life insurance companies (See Section 5 – Important Information). Provide Death Certificates.

- Life insurance and retirement accounts pass to named beneficiaries. Typically beneficiaries are required to complete a claim form and include a death certificate. Probate may not be necessary; consult with your legal advisors.

- The Social Security benefits received for the month of death or any subsequent months must be returned. For example, if a person dies in February, you must return the benefit paid in March. If benefits were paid by direct deposit, contact the bank or other financial institution and request that any funds received for the month of death or later be returned to Social Security. Do not cash any checks received for the month in which the person dies or later. Checks must be returned to Social Security as soon as possible.

  Eligible family members may be able to receive death benefits for the month in which the beneficiary died.

- If an estate(s) exceeds $2 million in 2006-2008 ($3.5 million in 2009) or the estate tax exemption available in the year of the death(s), the executor will be required to file a federal estate tax return(s) within 9 months from the date of death(s) and pay any estate taxes which are due at that time. The estate(s) can be valued at death or 6 months later, whichever is the most advantageous. Consult your accounting and legal advisors.

- Many states tax an estate—usually states which have income taxes, but not necessarily. Check your state.

GENERAL INFORMATION REGARDING PROBATE
PROBATE MAY VARY FROM STATE TO STATE.
CONSULT WITH YOUR PROFESSIONALS.

An executor is charged with the responsibility of carrying out the terms of the deceased's Will. This involves learning what the deceased owned at the time of his or her death; and according to the terms of his or her Will, carrying out the provisions thereof, i.e., determining the assets, paying any outstanding bills and distributing the remainder in accordance with the Will.

Contacting the deceased's attorney or hiring an attorney if the deceased does not have one is the executor's first action. Probate will then begin with a filing at the county court of the original Will and an application to serve as executor of the Will. Information about the deceased and any property owned will be included on the application. During a court hearing with the attorney, which should occur after a minimum 10-day waiting period, the judge will sign the order to admit the Will to probate. A signed document containing the executor's testimony will also be required.

In order to be able to sell real estate or close financial accounts, you will need "letters testamentary," which will be issued by the county clerk. These letters testamentary will authorize the executor to carry out the duties. As well, the executor will need to sign an oath stating that he or she will fulfill the duties as executor of the deceased's estate.

A Notice to Creditors must be prepared by the attorney within 30 days of receipt of the letters testamentary and must be published in a local newspaper. This will notify any creditors of the deceased's estate so that claims may be filed. Even if the deceased had no outstanding debts, this notice must be published.

The attorney will compile an inventory of the assets included in the deceased's Will. Since this list will not include any assets passing directly to named beneficiaries, as well as any real estate located outside the state in which the deceased resided, the inventory may be an incomplete list of the assets of the estate.

Items such as life insurance, certain types of joint bank or brokerage accounts, and retirement plans will pass directly to named beneficiaries without going through probate. A judge will sign an order after the inventory has been filed with the court to approve it.

In 2006-2008, if the estate's value exceeds $2 million ($3.5 million in 2009), the executor will be required to file a federal estate tax return within 9 months from the date of death and pay any estate taxes due at that time. Consult with your professionals regarding the estate tax exemption in your area in the year you are serving as executor.

NOTES:

SECTION 3

PERSONAL BILLS

Possible Needs:

Power of Attorney
Location_____

Other Documents
Location _____

Deposit Slips/Check
Location_____

In the event of incapacitation, signatory power, a Power of Attorney or another document(s) empowering legal action will be required in order to manage checking, savings, stock accounts, etc. After death, the executor will assume this responsibility. Consult with an attorney.

Remember that recurring bills need to be kept current, especially health, life, disability, auto, and homeowners insurance, as well as utilities, credit cards, etc. The deferral of these payments may result in the cancellation of policies and the discontinuation of services.

If a person is incapacitated, upon recovery he or she will resume his or her life. There is no need to put his or her financial situation in jeopardy due to failure to maintain his or her finances.

Consequently, by completing the Personal Bills section, your representative or executor will immediately know which bills need to be paid, the due date and the method of payment.

SECTION 3
PERSONAL BILLS

for _____

Last Update _____

Payee	Amount	Due Date	Pay Method	Explanation

SECTION 3
PERSONAL BILLS

for _____

Payee	Amount	Due Date	Pay Method	Explanation

NOTES:

SECTION 4

PASSWORDS

If your passwords are unavailable to your personal representative or executor, the ability to handle your finances will be greatly impaired. The following data sheet allows you or anyone entry into your banking, insurance or website accounts. Access will be necessary in order to maintain your financial matters.

Keep your passwords in a secure place. Should these passwords fall into the wrong hands, your credit and finances could be compromised.

SECTION 4
PASSWORDS

for _____

Last Update _____

Name of Company	User ID	Password	Pin #	Phone Password	Other

SECTION 4
PASSWORDS

for _____

Name of Company	User ID	Password	Pin #	Phone Password	Other

NOTES:

SECTION 5

IMPORTANT INFORMATION

Social Security, Passport & Driver's License Numbers

Accountant	**Attorney**	**Banking**
Banking Online	**Doctor**	**Financial Advisor**
Insurance	**Properties**	**Safe Deposit Box**
Stock Certificates	**Stock Accounts**	**Time Deposits**

If you are incapacitated or deceased, it will be necessary for your personal representative or executor to have the following information in order to contact your doctor and attorney, if you have one. Contacts for insurance, banking, financial advisors, safe deposit box(es), mortgage holders, and investment accounts will also be required.

This information should be kept in a safe place. Your credit and finances could be compromised if others are privy to it.

SECTION 5
IMPORTANT INFORMATION
for _____

Last Update _____

Social Security #														
Passport #														
Driver's License #														
ACCOUNTANT(S)	Phone #			Address			Email Address							
ATTORNEY(S)	Phone #			Address			Email Address							

SECTION 5
IMPORTANT INFORMATION
for _____

BANKING	Phone #	Contact	Account #	Checking/Saving	Checkbook Location

BANKING ONLINE	User ID	Password	Pin #	Phone Password	Account #

BIRTH CERTIFICATES	State of Birth	County of Birth	Dept. of Vital Statistics Address	Phone #	Location of Certificate

SECTION 5
IMPORTANT INFORMATION
for _____

	Phone #	Address	Email Address	Hospital	Other
DOCTOR(S)					
	Phone #	Address	Email Address	Account #	Cell #
FINANCIAL ADVISOR					
	Phone #	Address	Policy #	Group #	Policy Location
INSURANCE – AUTO					

SECTION 5
IMPORTANT INFORMATION
for _____

	Phone #	Address	Policy #	Group #	Policy Location
INSURANCE – DISABILITY					
INSURANCE - HEALTH	Phone #	Address	Policy #	Group #	Policy Location

SECTION 5
IMPORTANT INFORMATION
for _____

INSURANCE – LIFE/ TERM LIFE	Phone #	Policy #	Group #	Beneficiary(ies)	Policy Location

INSURANCE - LONG TERM CARE	Phone #	Address	Policy #	Group #	Policy Location

SECTION 5
IMPORTANT INFORMATION
for _____

INSURANCE – PROPERTY	Phone #	Policy #	Group #	Home / Rental / Vacation	Policy Location

INSURANCE- UMBRELLA	Phone #	Policy #	Group #	Type	Policy Location

SECTION 5
IMPORTANT INFORMATION
for _____

INSURANCE – OTHER	Phone #	Policy #	Group #	Type	Policy Location

MARRIAGE LICENSE	State of Marriage	County of Marriage	Dept. of Vital Statistics Address	Phone #	Location of License

SECTION 5
IMPORTANT INFORMATION
for _____

PROPERTIES - LOCATIONS	Mortgage Holder	Phone #	Loan #	Home / Rental / Vacation	Information Location
SAFE DEPOSIT BOX(ES)	Phone #	Address	Signatory(ies)	Box #	Key Location

SECTION 5
IMPORTANT INFORMATION
for _____

STOCK CERTIFICATES	Phone #	Contact	Address	Type	Location

SECTION 5
IMPORTANT INFORMATION
for _____

STOCKS	Phone #	Contact	Account #	IRA / 401K / Personal	Date Purchased

SECTION 5
IMPORTANT INFORMATION
for _____

TIME DEPOSITS	Account #	Amount and IRA / 401K / Personal	Maturity Date	Interest Rate	Information Location

SECTION 5
IMPORTANT INFORMATION
for _____

OTHER	Account #	Amount and IRA / 401K / Personal	Contact	Phone #	Information Location

NOTES:

SECTION 6

LOCATION OF ESTATE & MEDICAL DOCUMENTS

Possible Documents for this Section:

Bypass Trusts	**Directive to Physicians, Etc.**
Family Limited Partnership	**Irrevocable Trusts**
Living Will	**Medical Power of Attorney**
Power of Attorney	**Trusts**
Wills	**Other**

In the event of your incapacitation or death, one or more of the above documents may be required. The handling of your affairs will be facilitated for your personal representative or executor if he or she knows the location of the necessary documents.

SECTION 6
LOCATION OF ESTATE & MEDICAL DOCUMENTS
for _____

Last Update _____

Document	Location of Originals	Description	Contact	Phone #	Email

SECTION 6
LOCATION OF ESTATE & MEDICAL DOCUMENTS
for _____

Document	Location of Originals	Description	Contact	Phone #	Email

NOTES:

SECTION 7

CREDIT/DEBIT CARDS INFORMATION IN THE EVENT OF LOSS OR THEFT

When traveling, especially outside the U.S., leave your credit/debit card list with a reliable person or place in the room or hotel safe upon arrival at your destination. In the event your credit/debit cards are lost or stolen, customer service can be contacted. If traveling with your spouse, access to credit will still be available if you and your spouse carry different credit/debit cards.

Due to the fact that your credit/debit card information and finances could be compromised, keep this information in a secure place.

SECTION 7
CREDIT/DEBIT CARDS INFORMATION
for _____

Last Update _____

Credit/Debit Card	Credit/Debit Card #	U.S. Customer Service #	International Customer Service #

SECTION 7
CREDIT/DEBIT CARDS INFORMATION
for _____

Credit/Debit Card	Credit/Debit Card #	U.S. Customer Service #	International Customer Service #

NOTES:

SECTION 8

PERSONAL PROPERTY

Possible Categories:

Antiques	**Artwork**	**Books**
China	**Crystal**	**Furniture**
Glassware	**Jewelry**	**Knicknacks**
Paintings	**Sterling Silver**	**Other**

If your children are your heirs, do them a favor by assigning (as fairly and carefully as you can) personal property to them. Family is everything. Relationships are more important than things. However, when money and "things" are involved, relationships are often forgotten. Relieve your children of this possibility. Prepare your children and grandchildren for the future armed with integrity and compassion. Pitting them against one another does not serve them well.

SECTION 8
PERSONAL PROPERTY

for _____

Last Update _____

ITEM	RECIPIENT	DESCRIPTION

SECTION 8
PERSONAL PROPERTY

for _____

ITEM	RECIPIENT	DESCRIPTION

SECTION 8
PERSONAL PROPERTY

for _____

ITEM	RECIPIENT	DESCRIPTION

SECTION 8
PERSONAL PROPERTY

for _____

ITEM	RECIPIENT	DESCRIPTION

SECTION 8
PERSONAL PROPERTY

for _____

ITEM	RECIPIENT	DESCRIPTION

SECTION 8
PERSONAL PROPERTY

for _____

ITEM	RECIPIENT	DESCRIPTION

NOTES:

SECTION 9

FUNERAL & MEMORIAL SERVICES,
CONTACT NUMBERS FOR FAMILY & FRIENDS & OBITUARY

Contemplation of death is not a comfortable thought. Be that as it may, death will happen to all of us. In order to make the lives of your children, siblings and friends less stressful, prepare a list of your preferences regarding your funeral, the friends you would like to be contacted and any guests you would like to attend. Selection of your favorite readings, songs, speakers, etc., will relieve those planning your funeral of this job, and they will know that your wishes are being carried out.

Also, if information for your obituary is provided by you or if you have written the obituary, this emotional and time-consuming task will be easier for someone because of your forethought, or entirely unnecessary.

FUNERAL & MEMORIAL SERVICES, CONTACT NUMBERS FOR FAMILY & FRIENDS & OBITUARY

for _____

Last Update _____

	Contact	Phone #	Email	Location
FUNERAL HOME				
BURIAL				
CREMATION				
CHURCH				
OTHER VENUE				
MINISTER				

SECTION 9

FUNERAL & MEMORIAL SERVICES, CONTACT NUMBERS FOR FAMILY & FRIENDS & OBITUARY

for _____

	Contact	Phone #	Email	Location
BIBLE VERSES				
CATERER				
FOOD				

SECTION 9

FUNERAL & MEMORIAL SERVICES, CONTACT NUMBERS FOR FAMILY & FRIENDS & OBITUARY

for _____

	Contact	Phone #	Email	Location
FLOWERS				
MUSIC				

SECTION 9

FUNERAL & MEMORIAL SERVICES, CONTACT NUMBERS FOR FAMILY & FRIENDS & OBITUARY

for _____

	Contact	Phone #	Email	Location
ORDER OF SERVICE				
PALL BEARERS				

SECTION 9

FUNERAL & MEMORIAL SERVICES, CONTACT NUMBERS FOR FAMILY & FRIENDS & OBITUARY

for _____

	Contact	Phone #	Email	Location
POEMS				
RECEPTION				
SPEAKERS				

SECTION 9

FUNERAL & MEMORIAL SERVICES, CONTACT NUMBERS FOR FAMILY & FRIENDS & OBITUARY

for _____

CONTACTS	Contact	Phone #	Email	Location

SECTION 9
FUNERAL & MEMORIAL SERVICES, CONTACT NUMBERS FOR FAMILY & FRIENDS & OBITUARY
for _____

GUESTS	Contact	Phone #	Email	Location

SECTION 9
OBITUARY

for _____

Last Update _____

	Phone #	Fax or Email
Funeral Home		
Newspaper(s)		
	Information	Comments
Name		
Date of Birth		
Place of Birth		
Survivors:		
Spouse		

SECTION 9
OBITUARY

for _____

	Information	Comments
Children		
Parents		
Siblings		

SECTION 9
OBITUARY

for _____

Information	Comments
Grandparents	
Activities	
Funeral Home	

SECTION 9
OBITUARY

for _____

Donations	Information	Comments

NOTES:

SECTION 10

FAMILY HISTORY & GENEALOGY

While many people have been diligently recording information about their ancestors, all of us have not. By passing along the names, birth dates, and places of birth of your predecessors, generations following you will have access to valuable history.

The best gifts you can pass along are memories and anecdotes, those occurring when you were a child and stories told to you by your parents, grandparents and relatives. These are wonderful assets for your children and grandchildren.

SECTION 10
FAMILY HISTORY & GENEALOGY
for _____

Last Update _____

Name	Maiden Name	Birth Date	Place of Birth
Mother			
Father			
Maternal Grandmother			
Maternal Grandfather			
Fraternal Grandmother			

SECTION 10
FAMILY HISTORY & GENEALOGY
for _____

Name	Maiden Name	Birth Date	Place of Birth
Fraternal Grandfather			
Maternal Aunts			
Maternal Uncles			

SECTION 10
FAMILY HISTORY & GENEALOGY
for _____

Name	Maiden Name	Birth Date	Place of Birth
Fraternal Aunts			
Fraternal Uncles			

SECTION 10
FAMILY HISTORY & GENEALOGY
for _____

Name	Maiden Name	Birth Date	Place of Birth
Siblings			

NOTES:

GLOSSARY

ACCOUNTANT – A person or firm who keeps, audits, and inspects the financial records of individuals or businesses and prepares financial and tax reports.

ANNUITY CONTRACTS – A life insurance product that makes periodic payments for a specified period of time or for the rest of the annuitant's lifetime. There are two types of annuities: deferred and immediate. A deferred annuity allows financial assets to grow tax-deferred over time before being converted to payments to the annuitant. The payments from an immediate annuity begin within about a year of purchase.

ASSETS – Term used in accounting and business to denote property that has monetary value. Assets can be owned by an individual or a business and include financial holdings and real estate, and personal or intellectual property.

ATTORNEY - Someone who represents a person in the transaction of legal matters.

AUTO INSURANCE POLICY - Six types of coverage are available: a) bodily injury liability, for injuries the policyholder causes to someone; b) medical payments or Personal Injury Protection (PIP) for treatment of injuries to driver and passengers of policyholder's car; c) property damage liability, for damage policyholder causes to someone else's property; d) collision, for damage to policyholder's car from a collision; e) comprehensive, for damage to policyholder's car not involving a collision with another car (including damage from fire, explosions, earthquakes, floods, and riots), and f) uninsured motorists coverage, for costs resulting from an accident involving a hit-and-run driver or a driver who does not have insurance.

BENEFICIARY - The person or legal entity who receives money or other benefits from a benefactor. The beneficiary of a life insurance policy is the one who receives the payment of the amount of insurance after the death of the insured.

BOND - A bond is a debt security whereby the issuer borrows funds, usually from multiple sources for a stated purpose; the issuer is obliged to repay the principal with interest at specified intervals or at a later date. Other stipulations may also apply to the bond issue. Bonds are generally issued for terms longer than ten years.

BYPASS TRUST – This is a long-term planning device used to pass assets to the next generation's heirs. If property is left to a beneficiary in the form of a bypass trust, the property will not be subject to estate taxes when that person dies and the trust is established. The property will still be taxed in the estate(s) of the ultimate beneficiary(ies).

DEATH CERTIFICATE – A document issued by a local governmental department declaring the date, location and cause of a person's death. Each governmental jurisdiction prescribes the document form, and it is used for the purposes of arranging a burial or cremation, proving a person's Will or filing a claim on a person's life insurance.

DEFERRED COMPENSATION PLAN – This is an arrangement whereby a salaried employee defers a portion of his or her current earned income. The deferred income is invested, growing tax-deferred until a future date when the funds in the employee's account are distributed to him or her.

DEFINED BENEFITS - A defined benefit plan is any pension plan that pays a specified amount periodically to a retired employee. Traditional pension plans are defined benefit plans; they are controlled and the investment risk is assumed by the employer.

DEFINED CONTRIBUTION PLAN – Any plan with individual accounts. This plan provides for an individual account for each participant and for benefits based solely on the amount contributed to the account, plus or minus income, gains, expenses and losses allocated to the account. Contributions can be invested in certain categories of investment accounts, and the returns (positive or negative) on the investment are credited to the individual's account.

DIRECTIVE TO PHYSICIANS & FAMILY OR SURROGATES – A legal document designed to communicate your wishes regarding your medical treatment some time in the future.

DISABILITY INSURANCE – Insurance that will provide monthly income if the insured is unable to work because of illness or accident.

EXECUTOR - A legal term referring to the person named by the maker of a Will to carry out the directions of the Will.

FAMILY LIMITED PARTNERSHIP (FLP) - A limited partnership controlled by members of a family. As with other limited partnerships, the FLP has two types of partners: general and limited. General partners control all management and investment decisions and 100% of the liability is theirs. Limited partners are precluded from participating in the management of the FLP and have limited liability. The partnership itself is not taxable. However, the owners of a partnership report the partnership's income and deductions on their personal tax return, in proportion to their interests.

FAMILY MEDICAL HISTORY – List of illnesses affecting family, some of which may be genetic.

FINANCIAL ADVISOR - A professional who offers investment advice and financial planning services to individuals and businesses.

401(K) PLAN – An employer-sponsored retirement plan. A 401(k) plan allows a worker to save for retirement while deferring income taxes on the saved money and earnings until withdrawal. The employee elects to have a portion of his or her salary paid directly into his or her 401(k) account. In participant-directed plans, the employee can select from a number of investment options, usually an assortment of mutual funds emphasizing stocks, bonds, and money market investments, or a mix of the above. An employee can generally reallocate money among these investment choices at any time.

HEALTH INSURANCE - A type of insurance whereby the insurer pays the medical costs of the insured if the insured becomes sick due to covered causes or due to accidents, with insured paying designated premiums.

IRA - A retirement investment account that can be either an "individual retirement account" or an "individual retirement annuity." There are four types of IRAs: Traditional, Roth, Simple and SEP. Individual taxpayers establish Traditional and Roth IRAs, and they are allowed to contribute 100% of their compensation (self-employment income for sole proprietors and partners) up to a set maximum amount. Contributions to a Traditional IRA may be tax-deductible, depending upon the taxpayer's income, tax-filing status, and coverage by an employer-sponsored retirement plan. Roth IRA contributions are not tax-deductible. SEP and SIMPLE are retirement plans established by employers, and individual participant's contributions are made to these plans.

IRREVOCABLE TRUST - A trust that cannot be changed or canceled once initiated without consent of the beneficiary. Contributions cannot be taken out of the trust by the person establishing the trust. Irrevocable trusts offer tax advantages that revocable trusts do not by enabling a person to give money and assets away before he or she dies.

LETTERS TESTAMENTARY - A document issued by a probate court informing the executor of a Will of his or her appointment. This document empowers the executor to discharge the appointed responsibilities.

LIFE INSURANCE – A policy insuring the life of a specific person. Benefits are payable upon death of the insured.

LIVING WILL – An advanced health care document covering specific directives regarding the course of treatment caregivers should give and sometimes forbidding treatment should the person be unable to give their consent.

LONG-TERM CARE INSURANCE - An insurance product that helps provide for the cost of long-term care beyond a predetermined period. Long-term care insurance generally covers care that is not covered by health insurance, Medicare or Medicaid.

MEDICAL HISTORY – Information pertaining to one's past illnesses.

MEDICAL POWER OF ATTORNEY - Document signed by a competent adult designating a trusted person to make health care decisions on his or her behalf should he or she be unable to make such decisions.

OBITUARY – Newspaper notice of a person's death.

PASSWORDS – Selected codes for entry into online websites or certain accounts.

PERSONAL BILLS – Invoices or statements from entities to which a person owes money.

POWER OF ATTORNEY - Document that gives you the power to perform or undertake any action another person could perform or undertake if this person were present.

PROBATE - The legal process of settling the estate of a deceased person, specifically resolving all claims and distributing the deceased's property.

PROPERTIES - Real estate: homes, vacation houses, rental and commercial properties.

PROPERTY INSURANCE - Insurance that provides protection against most risks to property, such as fire, theft and some weather damage. Included are specialized forms of insurance, i.e., flood, fire, earthquake, and home insurance.

REAL ESTATE – Properties, such as land, residential, rental and commercial, owned by a person.

REVOCABLE TRUSTS – A trust that may be altered or terminated during the lifetime of the person who established the trust. Since the trust may be altered at any time until the person establishing the trust's death, it is considered part of that person's estate and is subject to taxation. Property is passed on to the beneficiaries only after the person establishing the trust's death, and at this point, the revocable trust becomes irrevocable.

SAFE DEPOSIT BOX – This safe is usually located in a bank vault and will often contain personal property such as jewelry or important documents (i.e., Wills, birth certificates, military records, passports, or property deeds) that a person would feel uncomfortable leaving at home in the event of theft, fire, flood or for other reasons.

SIGNATORY(IES) – Individual(s) other than account owner(s) who is/are authorized to effect transactions.

STOCKS - Capital raised in financial markets for a corporation or joint-stock company or held in a private corporation with possible restrictions or disposition by the issuance and distribution of shares. A person or organization holding at least a partial share of stock is called a stockholder.

STOCK CERTIFICATES - A legal document certifying ownership of a specific number of stock shares (or fractions thereof) in a corporation. Buying shares does not always lead to a stock certificate and may be held by a legal repository such as a securities dealer or brokerage house.

TERM LIFE INSURANCE – This type of insurance provides death protection for a stated time period. It is probably the simplest form of life insurance. Term insurance can be purchased in large amounts for a relatively small initial premium. It is suitable for short-term goals such as paying off a loan, or simply providing extra life insurance protection.

TIME DEPOSITS – Financial products with maturity dates, such as CDs, bonds, and U.S. treasuries.

TRUSTS – Body of law governing the management of personal affairs and the disposition of property of an individual in anticipation of the event of that person's incapacity or death.

UMBRELLA INSURANCE - Insurance giving you additional liability protection above and beyond your basic insurance.

U.S. TREASURIES - Government bonds issued by the United States Department of the Treasury through the Bureau of the Public Debt are debt financing instruments of the U.S. Federal Government. There are four types of treasury securities: savings bonds, treasury bills, treasury notes, treasury bonds.

VARIABLE ANNUITY - A contract between you and an insurance company, under which the insurer agrees to make periodic payments to you, beginning either immediately or at some future date. You purchase a variable annuity contract by making either a single purchase payment or a series of purchase payments.

WILL - A document by which a person regulates the rights of others over his property or family after death.

About the Author

Carole A. Wakefield was born and raised in the Deep South. Characteristics similar to those exhibited by Scarlet O'Hara in *Gone with the Wind* made their appearance early in her life. After living 40-plus years in Atlanta, Georgia, she and her family moved to Houston, Texas. Being a stay-at-home mom gave rise to many opportunities for organization. Consequently, while managing her husband's office, raising a teenage daughter, getting her son through college and being her mother's caregiver, she developed finely honed organizational skills.

At this time her husband was traveling internationally and she was responsible for the business as well as their personal lives. As she juggled these tasks, she began listing their personal information, e.g., banking, savings, insurance, investments, properties, etc., on her computer. Recently, after she mentioned the "Valuable Papers" to friends, they suggested that she publish a book. Making the "Valuable Papers" into a generic, all-purpose information book again required organizational skills. Her goal is to provide the tools for people to easily compile their important information and have it available to others in the event of their incapacitation or death, as well as have this information for their own use.

www.ingramcontent.com/pod-product-compliance
Lightning Source LLC
Chambersburg PA
CBHW060455060326
40689CB00020B/4540